Sounds Poems

Compiled by John Foster

Contents

Acknowledgements

The Editor and Publisher wish to thank the following who have kindly given permission for the use of copyright material:

John Foster for 'On rainy days' © 1995 John Foster; Julie Holder for 'Loud and soft' and 'Footsteps' both © 1995 Julie Holder; Ian Larmont for 'Sounds like me' © 1995 Ian Larmont; Daphne Lister for 'The echo bridge' © 1995 Daphne Lister; Tony Mitton for 'My big band' © 1995 Tony Mitton; Judith Nicholls for 'Can you hear?' © 1995 Judith Nicholls.

Sounds like me

Roar like a lion,
Squeak like a mouse.
Miaow like a cat
Locked out of a house.

Howl like a wolf,
Buzz like a bee.
Then shout, with your own voice,
'Hello! This is me!'

Ian Larmont

My big band

'Ting' went the triangle.
'Foo' went the flute.
'Whee' went the whistle.
The horn went 'Toot'.

Foo

Ting

Whee

Crash

Toot

Boom

Ta-ra

'Crash' went the cymbal.
'Boom' went the drum.
'Ta-ra' went the trumpet.
'Quiet!' yelled Mum.

Tony Mitton

Loud and soft

YOU MUST SHOUT
IF I'M FAR AWAY
SO I CAN HEAR
WHAT YOU WANT TO SAY.

But if you and I
Are near
You can whisper
And I will hear.

Julie Holder

The echo bridge

There's an old bridge
Where I sometimes go,
If I stand underneath it
And shout 'Hello!'

'Hello, hello, hello,'
I hear the call,
Yet there's no one else there –
Just me, that's all.

I roar like a lion
And one roars back,
I howl like a wolf
And I hear the whole pack.

I growl like a tiger
And more growls come,
It feels so scary –
I run back home to Mum.

Daphne Lister

Footsteps

Boots tramp,
Wellies stamp,
Slippers slap,
Flip-flops flap,
Trainers squeak
On shiny floors.
Bare feet pad, pad, pad,
Like paws.

Julie Holder

Can you hear?

The wind is a giant's breath,
I can hear him under my door.
He puffs and pants,
he moans and groans,
he whistles across my floor.

Judith Nicholls

On rainy days

The rain slaps and taps
against window panes.

The rain drops and plops
into puddles in lanes.

The rain giggles and gurgles
as it slurps down drains.

John Foster